D0531974

Ladybird Bible Stories

Noah's Ark

Moses

Joseph

David

Daniel

The First Christmas

The Lord's Prayer

The Lord Is My Shepherd

The Good Samaritan

The Prodigal Son

LADYBIRD BOOKS, INC.
Auburn, Maine 04210 U.S.A.
© LADYBIRD BOOKS LTD 1989
Loughborough, Leicestershire, England

All rights reserved. No part of this publication may be reproduced, stored in a retrieval system, or transmitted in any form or by any means, electronic, mechanical, photocopying, recording or otherwise, without the prior consent of the copyright owner.

Printed in England

The First
Christmas

retold by LYNNE BRADBURY

illustrated by JENNY WILLIAMS

Ladybird Books

A long time ago, Mary and Joseph had to leave their home in Nazareth and travel to Bethlehem.

It was a long, hard journey. Mary rode on a donkey, and Joseph walked beside her.

Mary was going to have a baby. An angel had come to tell her that she would have a baby boy, and that she should name him Jesus.

JERUSALEM
50
MILES

Mary knew that her baby would be born soon.

By the time they reached Bethlehem,
Mary and Joseph were very tired
and needed a place to sleep.

But the town was full of people…

…and everywhere Mary
and Joseph went…

…they were told that there
was no room for them.

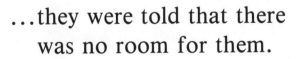

Then one innkeeper saw how tired Joseph and Mary were, and he remembered that he had a stable that was warm and dry. He said they could sleep there.

Joseph made a bed
of hay for Mary.

The donkey
and an ox
watched
over her.

That night Mary's baby was born.

They wrapped the baby Jesus in warm clothes...

and laid Him in a manger, where hay had been put for the animals.

On a hillside near Bethlehem, some shepherds
were watching over their sheep through the night.

Suddenly there was a bright light, and angels came to the shepherds.

One angel said, ''Don't be afraid. Jesus has been born. You will find Him in a stable in Bethlehem.''

The shepherds were very happy to hear the good
news. They went to Bethlehem to find the stable.

When they got there, they saw the baby Jesus
lying in the manger. Joseph and Mary were
watching over Him.

Far away in the East, a bright new star appeared in the sky.

Three Wise Men saw the star. They knew it was there to tell them that a new baby king had been born.

Night after night they followed the star...

until it stopped over the stable where Jesus had been born.

The three Wise Men went into the stable and saw their baby king.

They gave him presents
of gold, frankincense,
and myrrh before they
left to go back to their
own land.